Glyphs* & Math
(*short for hieroglyphics)

How to Collect, Interpret, and Analyze Data

BY TORRIE GUZZETTA AND PAT GILBERT

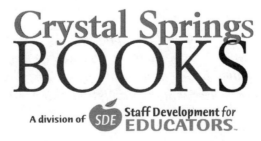

Crystal Springs
BOOKS

A division of SDE **Staff Development** *for* **EDUCATORS**

Peterborough, New Hampshire

Published by Crystal Springs Books
A division of Staff Development for Educators (SDE)
10 Sharon Road, PO Box 500
Peterborough, NH 03458
1-800-321-0401
www.crystalsprings.com
www.sde.com

ISBN-10:1-884548-80-6

ISBN-13:978-1-884548-80-2

Library of Congress Cataloging-in-Publication Data

Guzzetta, Torrie, 1959-

Glyphs* & math : how to collect, interpret, and analyze data / by Torrie Guzzetta and Pat Gilbert.

p. cm.

ISBN 1-884548-80-6

1. Hieroglyphics in Mathematics education. 2. Mathematics--Study and teaching. I. Title: Glyphs*
and math. II. Gilbert, Pat, 1949- III. Title.

QA20.H54G89 2005

510--dc22

2005019965

Editor: Sandra J. Taylor
Art Director, Designer, and Production Coordinator: Soosen Dunholter

Contents

INTRODUCTION **4**

STRAND-SKILL CHART **6**

APPLE GLYPH **8**
    (Collect and represent data in different forms)

Sports Shirt Glyph **14**
    (Place Value)

Pig Glyph **21**
    (Money)

Shape Up! Glyph **26**
    (Shape recognition and attributes)

Grandfather Clock Glyph **34**
    (Time)

Quilt Pattern Glyph **45**
    (Directional words)

Bare Bear Glyph **56**
    (Combinations)

Birth Announcement Glyph **65**
    (Length, weight, time)

Name Tag Glyph **76**
    (Money)

Pour Me Some More Glyph **87**
    (Capacity)

Introduction

WHAT IS A GLYPH?

Just as a graph conveys information from a chart or table, a glyph—short for hieroglyphic—is a form of picture writing that depicts information. The individual components of the finished glyph tell a story about the person who created it. Glyphs teach students to consult a legend, follow directions, and convey information about themselves. Glyphs also convey information about others.

A glyph has three key parts: a legend, or survey questions; directions that tell students what to draw, color, or write based on answers to questions; and a glyph pattern. The glyphs in this book have a fourth element—recording sheets. These sheets provide students with an opportunity to collect, interpret, and analyze data. Students will solve problems using number sense, measurement, geometry, algebra, proportional reasoning, and probability.

WHAT ARE THE BENEFITS OF USING GLYPHS?

The National Council of Teachers of Mathematics (NCTM) in *Curriculum and Evaluation Standards for School Mathematics* (1989) recommends that the mathematics curriculum include experiences with data that involve collecting, organizing, and describing data, as well as constructing, reading, and interpreting displays of data. In the process of exploring the finished glyphs, students are provided opportunities to communicate their mathematical thinking orally and in writing.

HOW SHOULD GLYPHS BE INTRODUCED TO STUDENTS?

Students who are unfamiliar with glyphs or who may need help reading the survey questions will benefit from a step-by-step approach. We recommend you make transparencies of the glyph patterns, legends, and recording sheets so you can project these using your overhead. Seeing the glyph constructed and modeled will help students visualize and understand the process. After reading each survey question, show the students how you circled your answer and then added the corresponding detail to your glyph pattern. Before you have them do their own, we suggest that you cover your completed glyph so that the students do not duplicate your example.

Reread the first survey question to the class and allow the students time to circle their choices and add the detail to their glyphs as it pertains to them. Continue the procedure of having students respond to one survey question at a time.

Be sure to have your students write their names on their legends and recording sheets in the spaces provided, and on the backs of their glyphs. Then you can keep track of their materials and know what belongs to whom.

HOW MUCH TIME DO YOU ALLOW FOR A GLYPH, AND HOW OFTEN SHOULD YOU USE THEM?

The glyphs in this book are arranged from simplest to hardest, so the time required for each one varies from glyph to glyph. The Apple Glyph, for example, could be completed in two days, but the Name Tag Glyph could take an entire week. Time also will depend on whether the glyph is being used to reinforce math skills already taught or to introduce a new math concept(s). After completing the legend (or survey questions), you could set aside one day a week to complete the recording sheets and extension activities and/or to investigate the literature connections that accompany the glyph.

How often you use glyphs will depend on you, the grade level you teach, and the ability of your students.

WHY LITERATURE CONNECTIONS?

In the April 2005 issue of *Instructor* magazine, Marilyn Burns discusses how children's books can be a great math teaching tool (see "Three Lessons: Using Storybooks to Teach Math"). She feels that connecting math to literature can boost the confidence of those students who love books but are "math-wary." Children's books spark students' imaginations in ways that textbooks or workbooks often don't, and they also help teachers integrate mathematics into their literature program.

△Warning:

We firmly believe that the glyphs and accompanying materials provided in this book will give your students a better understanding of math concepts. At the same time, they will have fun while learning mathematics.

Strand-Skill Chart

STRAND-SKILL	Apple	Sports Shirt	Pig	Shape Up!	Grandfather Clock	Quilt	Bare Bear	Birth Announcement	Name Tag	Pour Me Some More
NUMBER										
Understand and use place value		◊		◊						
Read, write, compare numbers/words 0–99		◊		◊				◊		◊
Round numbers to nearest 10		◊							◊	
Use ordinals					◊					
Odd/even		◊			◊			◊		◊
Skip count by	5s					1s 5s, 10s				
Find sums				◊		◊			◊	◊
Find differences								◊		
Concept of 1/2				◊	◊	◊			◊	1/4
Fractional words					◊	◊			◊	◊
Fraction symbols					◊	◊			◊	
Inverse addition/subtraction					◊				◊	
Separate into equal groups							◊			
Recognize pennies, nickels, dimes, and their values			◊						◊	
Make change			◊						◊	
MEASUREMENT										
Estimate weight as more/less than a pound	◊									
Distinguish hour/minute hands					◊					
Read clocks to the 1/2 hour, 5-minute intervals					◊			◊		
Elapsed time					◊					
Use a balance to compare weights	◊									
Estimate/measure length to the nearest inch		◊		◊		◊	◊	◊	◊	
Estimate/measure length in centimeters			◊		◊					
Area-counting squares						◊	◊			

GLYPH	Apple	Sports Shirt	Pig	Shape Up!	Grandfather Clock	Quilt	Bare Bear	Birth Announcement	Name Tag	Pour Me Some More
Conversions						in/yd	in/ft ft/yd	mo/yr oz/lb	in/yd	c/pt pt/qt
Perimeter				◊	◊	◊		◊	◊	
GEOMETRY										
Identify 2-D shapes		◊		◊	◊	◊			◊	
Recognize figures that are exactly alike			◊						◊	
Quadrilaterals									◊	
Understand the attributes of	ball				square rectangle	square rectangle				
Directional words					◊	◊				
DATA/CHANCE										
Pictograph					◊					
Collect and interpret data	◊	◊	◊	◊	◊	◊	◊	◊	◊	◊
Create a glyph by answering a survey	◊	◊	◊	◊	◊	◊	◊	◊	◊	◊
Understand how to group tally marks	◊			◊	◊	◊	◊			
Bar graph						◊	◊			◊
Use charts/graphs to answer questions	◊	◊	◊	◊	◊	◊			◊	
Venn diagram	◊					◊				
Line plot		◊							◊	
Make predictions						◊			◊	
Understand middle					◊					
More/less likely		◊		◊	◊				◊	◊
Possible selections								◊	◊	
ALGEBRA										
Understand 1-to-1 correspondence	◊									
Understand 1-to-several correspondence				◊				◊		
Proportional reasoning						◊			◊	
Recognize and continue patterns					◊					
Complete number sentences		◊	◊							◊

Apple Glyph

OBJECTIVES

◎ Create a glyph by answering a survey of questions
◎ Understand how to group tally marks
◎ Skip count by fives
◎ Collect, organize, and interpret data
◎ Understand one-to-one correspondence
◎ Estimate weight of real objects as more or less than a pound
◎ Use balance to compare weights of objects
◎ Understand the attributes of a ball/sphere

STUDENT MATERIALS

Per Student:

Apple Pattern, Legend, and Recording Sheets

Markers or crayons

Paper towel

TEACHER MATERIALS

Transparencies:
Apple Pattern, Legend, and Recording Sheets

Apples: Granny Smith, Red Delicious, and Golden Delicious

Knife

Enlarged Tally Chart (or transparency)

Enlarged Pictograph (or transparency)

Venn diagram (or transparency)

1-pound item, such as bag of dried beans, box of confectioners' sugar, box of baking soda, etc.

Balance

2 uncut oranges

2 uncut apples

Note: Check with your school nurse before doing this activity to make sure there are no food allergies.

PROCEDURE

1. Cut up enough of each type of apple so every student will have a sample of all three types. Place each sample on a paper towel and distribute them to the students. Ask students to taste each type of apple.

2. Distribute the recording sheets to the students and ask them to write their names at the top.

3. Using the enlarged tally chart (or transparency), record the students' votes for their favorite type of apple and tell them to transfer this information to their recording sheets. (Ask questions that could be answered by looking at the tally chart, such as: What is our class's favorite type of apple? Did Granny Smith get an odd or even number of votes? How many people voted in our class?)

4. Distribute the Apple Legend and Pattern to students. Have them fill in the blanks, circle their answers to each question, and then create their glyphs. Ask students to write their names on the backs of their glyphs.

5. Have students refer to their glyphs and then organize themselves according to their favorite type of apple. Point out to students that they have created a human pictograph.

6. Post glyphs to represent data collected in the human pictograph and have students fill in the pictograph on their recording sheets. Point out to them that their tally charts and their pictographs represent the same information.

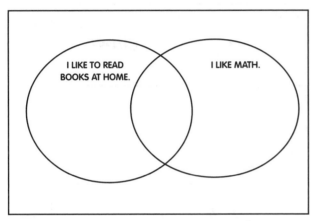

7. Post (or project) the Venn diagram. Using information from the glyphs, mark an "X" to show each student's response on the Venn. (**Note:** For those students who do not like to read books at home and do not like math, mark an "X" outside the circles.) Ask students to copy this information on their recording sheets.

8. Compare and contrast data on the Venn diagram, and have students complete #3a–#3c on their recording sheets.

9. Have students use an apple to determine whether it weighs more or less than a 1-pound item and to check their predictions with a balance. Ask students to complete #4 on their recording sheets.

10. Talk about why an apple would not fit into the 3-D category of a ball/sphere.

Explain that if a ball/sphere is cut in half vertically or horizontally, it will have a face on each hemisphere in the shape of a circle. This is not true of an apple. Prove it by cutting one orange and one apple in half vertically and then cutting the remaining orange and apple in half horizontally. The faces of the oranges, no matter which way they were cut, will have the shape of a circle. The faces of the apples will have the shape of a circle only when cut horizontally. Ask students to complete #5 on their recording sheets and to pass their completed sheets in to you.

EXTENSION

Give different items to the students to place on a balance and then compare the weight to that of an apple and/or something that weighs 1 pound.

LITERATURE CONNECTIONS

Tally O'Malley by Stuart J. Murphy

Arctic Fives Arrive by Elinor J. Pinczes

Apple Legend

1. What is your favorite type of apple?_____

	Granny Smith	Red Delicious	Golden Delicious
Color of your apple	**green**	**red**	**yellow**

2. Do you like math? _____

	Yes	No
Color of your leaf and stem	**green**	**brown**

3. Do you read books at home?_____

	Yes	No
Color of your worm	**orange**	**blue**

Apple
Pattern

Apple Recording Sheet

1. Use the class's glyphs to fill in the tally chart below.

Favorite Type of Apple Tally Chart

Green (Granny Smith)	
Red (Red Delicious)	
Yellow (Golden Delicious)	

2. Use the tally chart to fill in the pictograph below.

Favorite Type of Apple Pictograph

Green (Granny Smith)	
Red (Red Delicious)	
Yellow (Golden Delicious)	

☺ = 1 person

3. Use the class's glyphs to fill in the Venn diagram below.

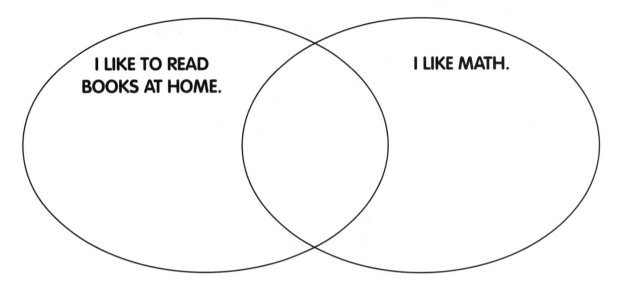

a. The number of students who like to read books at home is
_____ the number of students who like math.

(greater than) (less than) (equal to)

b. The number of students who don't like math is _____
the number of students who don't read   (greater than) (less than) (equal to)
books at home.

c. Use the glyphs to help you make a prediction. If a new student

joined your class today, finish the following sentence:

I think he/she would like _____ apples, he/she

_____ like to read books at home, and he/she

_____ like math.

4. My apple weighed _____ a pound.

(greater than) (less than) (the same as)

5. An apple is not a ball/sphere because _____

_____.

Sports Shirt Glyph

OBJECTIVES

◎ Create a glyph by answering a survey of questions
◎ Collect and interpret data
◎ Understand and use place value
◎ Determine if a number is odd or even
◎ Read, write, and compare numbers through 99
◎ Round numbers to the nearest 10
◎ Use real situations to determine what is more or less likely to happen
◎ Identify geometric shapes
◎ Complete number sentences
◎ Estimate length to the nearest inch

STUDENT MATERIALS

Per Student:

Sports Shirt Pattern, Legend, and Recording Sheets

Markers or crayons

TEACHER MATERIALS

Transparencies:
Sports Shirt Pattern, Legend, and Recording Sheets

Coaches' Shirts (with one of the following numbers written on each: 0, 10, 20, 30, 40, 50, 60, 70, 80, 90, 100)

Clothesline and clothespins

PROCEDURE

1. Distribute the Sports Shirt Legend and student Sports Shirt Pattern to students. Have them answer each question, follow the directions, and create their glyphs. Ask them to write their names on the backs of their glyphs.

2. Hang a clothesline in a convenient and accessible location, and place a container of clothespins nearby.

3. Have two students come up with their Sports Shirt glyphs and compare their favorite numbers. Ask them to pretend the clothesline is a number line and to hang their numbers in the correct order. Then call on another student and have her determine where her number belongs on the clothesline. Continue until all students have placed their shirts on the clothesline.

4. Distribute the Sports Shirt Recording Sheets and have students write their names at the top of each page and then answer #1–#4.

5. If it is appropriate for your grade level, ask students to find two shirts that would have a sum close to 50 and/or a sum close to 100.

6. Take down the glyphs and return them to the students.

7. Put up the Coaches' shirts. Tell students they will find out which team they are on by rounding their numbers to the nearest multiple of 10. Call students up one at a time and ask them which two multiples of 10 their number is between. Then have each student say which one his number is closer to and pin his shirt underneath that multiple of 10. (Example: If the student's number is 26, he should say "26 is between the two multiples of 10—20 and 30. It is 6 spaces away from 20 and 4 spaces away from 30, so it is closer to 30.") **Note:** Do not teach students to round down when a number ends in a 0–4 and to round up when a number ends in a 5–9. Instead, the only rule they need to know is this: when a number ends in a 5, it is an equal distance from both multiples of 10, so round up to the nearest multiple of 10. Continue until all students have had a turn, and then have them complete #5–#6 on their recording sheets.

8. Ask students to name all the numbers that would hang under each Coach's shirt. (Example: If 20 is the number, shirts numbered from 15–24 would hang underneath.)

9. Ask students to complete #7–#9 on their recording sheets and then hand them in to you.

LITERATURE CONNECTIONS

Missing Mittens by Stuart J. Murphy

Inch by Inch by Leo Lionni

Where the Sidewalk Ends, "One Inch Tall," by Shel Silverstein

Sports Shirt Legend

1. What is your favorite two-digit number? _____

Choose the color that shows if you are a boy or girl. Using this color, write your favorite two-digit number in the middle of your shirt pattern.	Girl	Boy
	red	blue

2. Is your favorite two-digit number odd or even? _____

My favorite two-digit number is...	Odd	Even
	underline your number	circle your number

3. You have been on what type of sports team? _____

Draw the shape on the sleeves of your shirt that shows the answer to the question. If you have been on more than one team, pick your favorite.	Baseball or Softball	Soccer	Other	None
	●	■	▲	leave sleeves blank

4. Do you like to play sports? _____

	Yes	No
Write your last name across the top of your shirt pattern.	all capital letters	capitalize the first letter only

Sports Shirt
Pattern—Student

Sports Shirt Pattern—Coach

NAME: _____

Sports Shirt
Recording Sheet

1. My favorite two-digit number is _____.

2. My number has _____ ten(s) and _____ one(s).

3. Write the number word for your favorite number.

_____

4. My number is greater than _____'s but less than
   _____ (a student's name)
   _____'s.
   (a student's name)

5. My number is between these two multiples of ten: _____ and _____.

6. The multiple of 10 that my number is closer to is _____.

7. Make a line plot by placing an "X" above each shape to show
   how many students were on each type of sports team.

● circle	■ square	▲ triangle	no shape
(baseball or softball)	(soccer)	(other)	(no team)

8. Look at the letters in your last name.

   a. I have _____ letters in my last name.

   b. I have _____ vowels in my last name.

   c. I have _____ consonants in my last name.

   d. The number of vowels is _____ the number
   of consonants.   (greater than) (less than) (equal to)

   e. Pretend that you put all the letters of your last name in a bag
   and picked one without looking. You are _____ likely
   to pick a consonant than a vowel.   (more) (less) (equally)

   f. Complete the number sentences below.

   _____ + _____ = _____
   (number of vowels   (number of consonants   (number of letters
     in last name)   in last name)   in last name)

   _____ + _____ = _____
   (number of consonants   (number of vowels   (number of letters
     in last name)   in last name)   in last name)

9. Using your inch benchmark, estimate the distance from the top
   to the bottom of your sports shirt.

   The estimated distance

   is _____ inches.

   (Remember, the
   benchmark for an
   inch is the distance
   across the tops of
   your first two fingers.)

Pig Glyph

OBJECTIVES

- ◎ Create a glyph by answering a survey of questions
- ◎ Collect and interpret data
- ◎ Recognize figures that are exactly alike
- ◎ Estimate length using centimeters
- ◎ Recognize pennies, nickels, dimes, and their relative values; use "¢" symbol
- ◎ Make change using up to three types of coins at one time
- ◎ Complete number sentences

STUDENT MATERIALS

Per Student:

Pig Pattern and Recording Sheets

Markers or crayons

Scissors

Glue

TEACHER MATERIALS

Transparencies:
  Pig Pattern and
  Recording Sheets

Play coins

Items for store priced from
  1¢ to 15¢ (pencils, erasers,
  sheets of paper, etc.)

PROCEDURE

1. Distribute the Pig Recording Sheets and Pattern. Talk about the concept of "exactly alike." Have students write their names at the top of their recording sheets and complete #1.

2. Using the centimeter benchmark (about the width of the little finger), have students estimate the distance across the pig and then complete #2 on their recording sheets.

3. Have students complete #3–#4 on their recording sheets.

4. Using your last name, model how to complete #5a–#5c. Then have students complete #5a–#5c on their sheets.

5. Set up a store with items that are priced from 1¢ to 15¢. Model how to complete #6a-#6d. Select play coins that match the coins at the bottom of the piggy bank. Then have each student choose an item to purchase from the store. Walk students through the role of playing cashier or customer:

   The customer bought an item that cost _____¢.

   He/she paid for that item using _____.

Should he/she get any change back? _____.

If so, count back change by adding on.

Examples:

My last name is Guzzetta. Guzzetta = 8¢

I have a nickel and 3 pennies to buy an item. If I bought an eraser for 5¢, I would use a nickel to pay for the item. I would not get back any change.

My last name is Terry. Terry = 5¢

I have a nickel to buy an item. If I bought a Tootsie Roll for 3¢, I would use a nickel to pay for the item, and I would get back change. I would get back two pennies.

6. Now show students how to fill out #6a–#6d on the recording sheet. Have students take turns coming up and buying one item. You or another student can play the cashier. Have students record their actions on #6a–#6d.

7. Ask students to complete #7 on their recording sheets.

8. Post the pig glyphs that show the numerical value of the pennies in the piggy bank. Have students complete #8 on their recording sheets.

9. Post the remaining glyphs. Have students match two glyphs that have the same value represented with different coin combinations.

EXTENSION

Have a student come up and buy as <u>many items as possible</u> using the value of his/her last name.

LITERATURE CONNECTIONS

Alexander, Who Used to Be Rich Last Sunday by Judith Viorst

The Coin Counting Book by Rozanne Lanczak Williams

The Penny Pot by Stuart J. Murphy

Pig
Patterns

Pig Recording Sheet

1. Are your two pigs exactly alike? _____

   How do you know? _____

   _____

2. Using your centimeter benchmark, estimate the distance across your pig from the tip of his nose to where his tail starts.

   The estimated distance is _____centimeters.

3. Have you ever seen a real pig? (TV doesn't count.) _____

	Yes	No
Color each pattern	**pink**	**yellow**

4. Have you ever touched a real pig? (Stuffed animals don't count.) _____

	Yes	No
Eyes on pigs	**Draw eyes on your pigs**	**Do not draw eyes on your pigs**

5. How many letters are in your last name?_____

   a. Cut out one penny for every letter in your last name. Glue them on the top piggy bank.

   b. Write the value of the pennies on the top piggy bank. My piggy bank has _____cents in it.

   c. Cut out the fewest coins possible that would equal the amount of money in your top piggy bank. Glue the coins on the bottom piggy bank.

6. a. When I went to the store, I bought a _____.

b. It cost _____.

c. Draw the coin(s) used to pay for the item.

d. I _____ get back change. If you did, draw your change.
   (did) (did not)

7. Cut out the pigs, write your first and last names on back of both, and give them to your teacher.

8. Look at the posted pigs.

a. How many pigs are posted? _____

b. How many students have seen a real pig? _____

c. How many students have not seen a real pig? _____

d. Complete the number sentences below.

| _____ | + | _____ | = | _____ |
| (students who have seen a real pig) | | (students who have not seen a real pig) | | (number of pigs posted) |

| _____ | + | _____ | = | _____ |
| (students who have not seen a real pig) | | (students who have seen a real pig) | | (number of pigs posted) |

Shape Up! Glyph

OBJECTIVES

◎ Create a glyph by answering a survey of questions

◎ Collect and interpret data

◎ Identify 2-D shapes by their sides and corners

◎ Find sums

◎ Understand the concept of half

◎ Find the distance around a shape

◎ Use rulers to find lengths in inches

◎ Identify events that certainly will happen or definitely will not happen

◎ Describe what is more likely or less likely to happen

◎ Use one-to-several correspondence in real situations

◎ Collect information and represent it using tally marks

◎ Collect information and represent it using a pictograph

◎ Create questions that can be answered using a chart

◎ Read, write, count, and compare number words one through thirty

◎ Develop an understanding of place value for ones and tens

STUDENT MATERIALS

Per Student:

Shape Up! Pattern, Legend, and Recording Sheets

Popsicle sticks

Markers or crayons

Scissors

Tape

Yarn or string

TEACHER MATERIALS

Transparencies:
   Shape Up! Pattern, Legend, and Recording Sheets

Enlarged pictograph on a poster

Smiley Face stickers (or any sticker that has symmetry)

PROCEDURE

1. Distribute the Shape Up! Legend and Pattern to students and ask them to write their names at the tops of the legend pages. Have them fill in the blanks, circle their answers to each question, and then create their glyphs.

2. Hand out Shape Up! Recording Sheets and have students complete questions #1–#4.

3. Hand out string and scissors. Ask students to lay string around the outside of their shapes and cut the string so that it represents the distance around their shapes. Then have them measure the string to the nearest inch. Next, ask students to tape their strings on the board under the appropriate heading: Square, Circle, Rectangle, or Triangle. Ask them what they notice about the lengths of the strings. (The strings should all be about the same length: 12 inches.) Have students complete #5–#7 on their recording sheets.

4. Collect and post the glyphs.

5. Have students complete #8–#9 on their recording sheets. (**Note:** For 8a., you are certain to pick every shape that was put into the bag; for 8d., it is impossible to pick any shape that was not put into the bag.)

6. Use the glyphs to gather information to make a pictograph. A great way to do this is to make a large pictograph on a poster. Have students line up according to how they voted and then pair off in twos within that line. Give each pair a sticker and tell them to use one sticker for every two votes. Have them come up and post their sticker in the appropriate space on the pictograph. Students have to solve the problem of what to do if they have an odd number of students for a certain category. (They will naturally say to cut the sticker in half.) This activity is worth the time it takes. Students understand the one-to-two correspondence on the pictograph, and they realize that each sticker represents two of the students in their class. They also understand that half a sticker represents one student. Now ask students to fill out #10–#11 on their recording sheet.

7. Tell students to collect information from the glyphs and fill in the tally chart for #12. Then have them write two questions (#13) that could be answered by looking at the tally chart. Call on students to share their questions.

8. Post (or project) a completed Shape Up! pattern and have students answer #14 on their own. This will assess whether or not they understand how to interpret a legend.

LITERATURE CONNECTIONS

Shapes by Henry Pluckrose

The Greedy Triangle by Marilyn Burns

A Light in the Attic, "Shapes," by Shel Silverstein

The Tangram Magician by Lisa Campbell Ernst

Shape Up! Legend

1. What is your favorite subject in school? _____

	Math	Reading	Science	Spelling
Circle the shape that shows your favorite subject.	△	○	▭	□

2. What do you do for lunch?_____

	Eat cafeteria food	Bring lunch from home
Color the border of your shape	**red**	**green**

3. What is your favorite thing to do after school? _____

	Watch TV	Play with friends	Play video games	Ride my bike
Color your shape	**pink**	**yellow**	**orange**	**white**

4. I _____forget to do my homework.

	Always	Sometimes	Never
Draw the design in your shape	○○○	◇◇◇	★★★

5. Cut out your shape, write your first and last names on the back, and tape it on a Popsicle stick.

Shape Up!
Pattern

NAME: _____

Shape Up!
Recording Sheet

1. The name of my shape is a _____. It has _____ sides and _____ corners.

2. How many students picked one of the subjects below as their favorite? (Raise your shape piece to vote.)

   a. Favorite subject is math _____

   b. Favorite subject is reading _____

   c. Favorite subject is science _____

   d. Favorite subject is spelling _____

3. How many students voted? _____

4. More than half of the class picked science as their favorite subject. Is this statement true? _____

   Explain how you know. _____

   _____

5. Lay a piece of string around the outside of your shape. Cut it to fit exactly around your shape. Measure the length of your string to the nearest inch. _____

   Tape your string on the board under the name of your shape.

6. What do you notice about the lengths of all the strings?

_____

_____

7. The distance around the circle, square, triangle, and rectangle is
   about _____ inches.

8. a. If you put all the shapes into a bag, which shape are you
      certain to pick?_____

   b. If you put all the shapes into a bag, which shape are you
      most likely to pick?_____

   c. Which shape are you least likely to pick? _____

   d. Which shape is it impossible to pick? _____

9. Do more students eat cafeteria food or bring their lunch from
   home? _____

   _____ eat cafeteria food   _____ bring their lunch
   (number)   (number)

   _____   _____
   (number word)   (number word)

   _____ _____   _____ _____
   (tens)   (ones)   (tens)   (ones)

   _____ is greater than _____because

   _____

10. Gather the information needed to make a pictograph showing the results of what our class likes to do after school.

After-school Activities   Number of Students

Watch TV	
Play with friends	
Play video games	
Ride my bike	

After-school Activities Pictograph

Watch TV	
Play with friends	
Play video games	
Ride my bike	

☺ = 2 votes

11. Describe in words what you drew if there was an odd number of votes.

_____

_____

12. Fill in the tally chart to show how many students forget to do their homework.

Forgets to Do Homework	Tally Marks
Always	
Sometimes	
Never	

13. Write two questions that could be answered using the information in the tally chart.

a._____

_____

b. _____

_____

14. What can you tell about the student from the completed glyph pattern that is displayed?

_____

_____

_____

Grandfather Clock Glyph

OBJECTIVES

◎ Create a glyph by answering a survey of questions

◎ Collect and interpret data

◎ Identify 2-D shapes; number of sides and corners

◎ Compare and contrast the attributes of a square and a rectangle

◎ Recognize and continue patterns in objects

◎ Use ordinals

◎ Understand the middle of a line

◎ Use a centimeter ruler to measure height and width of a figure

◎ Use directional words

◎ Find the perimeter of a figure using nonstandard units

◎ Distinguish hour and minute hands on a clock

◎ Read standard clocks to the nearest hour, half-hour, quarter-hour, or 5-minute interval

◎ Solve problems involving elapsed time

◎ Recognize even and odd numbers

◎ Understand and use fractional words to represent a portion

◎ Use symbols to represent fractions in situations

◎ Understand the concept of half

◎ Understand the inverse relationship of addition and subtraction

◎ Represent information collected using tallies

◎ Describe what is more likely, less likely, or certain to happen in a real situation

STUDENT MATERIALS

Per Student:

Grandfather Clock Pattern, Legend, and Recording Sheets #1, #2, and #3

Markers or crayons

Centimeter ruler

TEACHER MATERIALS

Transparencies:
   Grandfather Clock Pattern, Legend, and Recording Sheets #1, #2, and #3

Clothesline

Clothespins

Display clock

24 cards of two different colors (12 of each)

Red, blue, yellow, and green colored tiles or cubes (not more than 12 of each color)

Bag to hold the tiles or cubes

PROCEDURE

1. Create 24 clock-hour cards: Make 12 cards of one color showing 12:00 midnight to 11:00 A.M; make 12 cards of the other color showing 12:00 noon to 11:00 P.M.

2. Distribute the Grandfather Clock Recording Sheet #1, Pattern, and centimeter ruler to each student. Ask them to write their names at the tops of the recording sheets and then to complete Recording Sheet #1.

3. Project your transparency of this recording sheet and discuss it with the students, filling it in with their help.

4. Distribute the Grandfather Clock Legend and Recording Sheet #2 and ask students to write their names at the tops of the sheets. Make sure students know what the word "pendulum" means, and then have them complete the legend and #1–#3 on Recording Sheet #2.

5. Call on two students. Have them use their Recording Sheet #2 to compare clock times and pictures drawn to determine how to line up. (You may wish to use the clothesline and clothespins to display the order. Have students hang their pictures from the earliest event to the latest event depicted.) Ask students to read their times, show their pictures, and give their answers for #3. (If a student has problems answering #3 correctly, provide him with a display clock to manipulate.)

6. Call on another student and ask her to compare her clock time and picture, and to decide where to line up or hang her recording sheet on the clothesline. Have her give her answers for #3. Continue the procedure until the entire class has lined up or hung their recording sheets on the clothesline in time order, read their clock times, and given their answers to #3.

7. Pose these questions to the students:

   - What is the earliest time shown?

   - What is the latest time shown?

8. Return Recording Sheets #2 if they were hung on the clothesline. Ask students to complete #4–#5 and then discuss their answers.

9. Post (or project) a completed Grandfather Clock pattern and have students answer #6 independently. This will enable you to assess your students' ability to interpret the legend.

10. Using the clothesline, hang the 24 clock-hour cards in order. Call one student up at a time and have him bring his glyph. Ask the student which two hours his time is between and which hour his time is closer to. Then have him use clothespins or tape to attach his glyph below the hour card. Continue until all students have rounded their time to the nearest hour.

11. Pose this question to the students: What are all the times that would round to 7:00?

12. Distribute Recording Sheet #3 to each student. With the glyphs posted, have students complete #1–#3.

13. To test the answers to #3a–#3c, bring out the bag filled with the colored tiles. (**Note:** For #3c., you cannot be certain what color you will pull from the bag, but you can be certain that it will be one of the colors in the bag: red, blue, yellow, OR green.) Ask students to pull one tile from the bag, record the results in #3d, and return the tile to the bag. Continue this procedure until a total of 50 tiles has been pulled and recorded. Discuss the results (#3e).

LITERATURE CONNECTIONS

Teddy Bears Tell the Time by Staff of Brimax

The School Bus Comes at Eight O'clock by David McKee

The Grouchy Ladybug by Eric Carle

It's About Time, Max! by Kitty Richards, from the Math Matters Series

Time to … by Bruce McMillan

NAME: _____

Grandfather Clock
Legend

1. How many letters are in your last name?_____

2. Draw the **hour** hand on the Grandfather Clock Pattern to show the number of letters. (If there are 12 or more letters in your last name, use "12" on the clock face.)

3. How old are you? _____

   Draw the **minute** hand on the pattern to show your age.

4. In what month were you born? _____

	Dec. Jan. Feb.	Mar. Apr. May	June July Aug.	Sept. Oct. Nov.
Color of pendulum	red	blue	yellow	green

5. What day of the month is your birthday? _____

	Day of the month is an odd number	Day of the month is an even number
Draw this shape at the end of the pendulum.	△	○

6. Write your first and last names on the back of your glyph pattern.

Grandfather Clock
Pattern

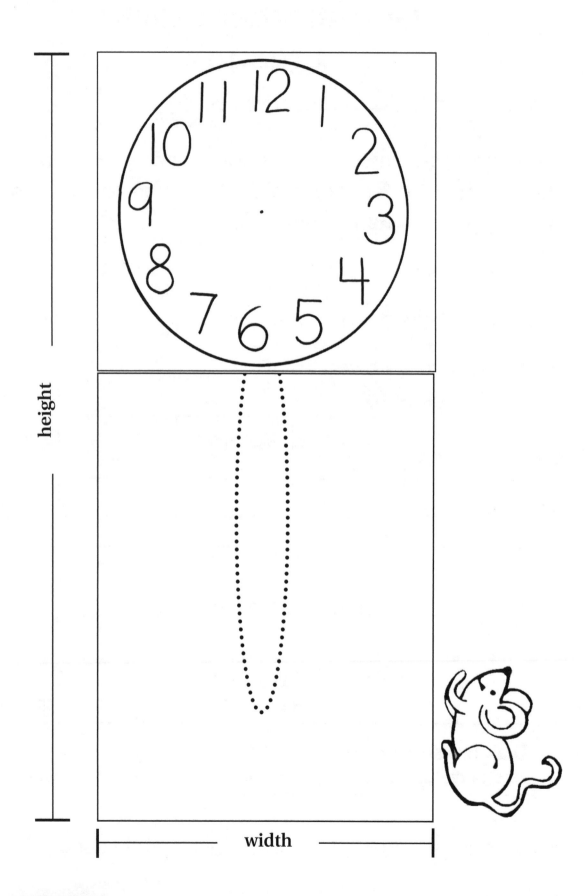

height

width

NAME: _____

Grandfather Clock
Recording Sheet #1

1. Name the shapes that are found in the Grandfather Clock Pattern. Give the number of sides and number of corners.

Shape	Sides	Corners
_____	_____	_____
_____	_____	_____
_____	_____	_____

2 a. Which two shapes are alike?

   _____   _____

   b. How are they alike? _____

   _____

   c. How are the two shapes different? _____

   _____

3. Study the pattern of shapes.

   ■ ▲ ● ● ● ■ _____ ● ● ● ■ ▲

   a. What shape goes in the empty space? _____

   b. If the pattern continues, what would follow the triangle?

   _____

4.

a. In what position is the triangle? _____

b. What object is in 2nd position? _____

c. How many objects are between the smiley face and

the star?_____

d. Which object is in the middle of the line? _____

e. If this is part of a line and you know that the rectangle is

10th in line, in what position is the heart? _____

5. Using a centimeter ruler, measure the width and height of

the clock.   width _____ height _____

6 a. In "Hickory, Dickory, Dock," what direction did the mouse run?

_____

(up)   (down)   (left)   (right)

b. The mouse pictured is about
4 centimeters in length. About how
many mice would it take to go
completely around the clock?

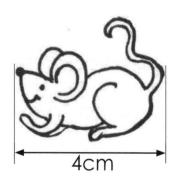

4cm

About_____ mice

Grandfather Clock
Recording Sheet #2

1. What time is shown on your clock? _____

2. Draw a picture showing what you could be doing at that time.
   Make sure your picture shows whether your activity is during the
   day or night.

3. After eating a meal, it is usually recommended that you wait
   1 hour to swim and 2 hours to go jogging. Complete the table.

Time on your clock	You may swim at	You may jog at

4. Read and record the times on the clocks below.

_____   _____   _____

5. Jacob looks at his watch. He needs to meet Taylor at the soccer field in 20 minutes. What time will he arrive at the soccer field?

_____

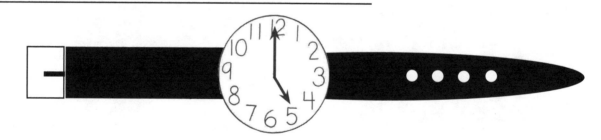

6. What can you tell about the student from the completed Grandfather Clock Pattern that is displayed?

_____

_____

_____

What can't you tell about the student from the completed pattern?

_____

NAME: _____

Grandfather Clock
Recording Sheet #3

1. Use the glyphs to answer the following questions:

   a. How many glyphs are posted? _____

   b. How many students were born on a day of the month that is an odd number? _____

   c. What portion of the students were born on a day of the month that is an odd number?

   _____   _____
   (words)   (symbol)

   d. The fraction is _____ half.
                      (less than) (greater than) (equal to)

   e. How do you know? _____

2. Complete the number sentences.

                    +   **=**

   _____   _____   _____
   (number of students born   (number of students born   (number of glyphs posted)
   on a day of the month   on a day of the month
   that is an even number)   that is an odd number)

                    -   **=**

   _____   _____   _____
   (number of glyphs posted)   (number of students born   (number of students born
                                      on a day of the month   on a day of the month
                                      that is an odd number)   that is an even number)

3. Fill in the chart below. Use tally marks to record the number of students.

Month of Birth	Number of Students	Number of Color Tiles Equals Number of Students
Dec. Jan. Feb.		Red
Mar. Apr. May		Blue
June July Aug.		Yellow
Sept. Oct. Nov.		Green

a. Which color tile are you least likely to pull out of the bag?

_____

b. Which color tile are you most likely to pull out of the bag?

_____

c. Which color tile are you certain to pull out of the bag?

_____

d. As a tile is pulled from the bag, record the results.

Colors	Tally Marks	Total
Red		
Blue		
Yellow		
Green		

e. Do the results above match your answers in #3a–#3c?

_____

Quilt Pattern Glyph

OBJECTIVES

◎ Create a glyph by answering a survey of questions

◎ Collect and interpret data

◎ Identify 2-D shapes; number of sides and corners

◎ Compare and contrast the attributes of a square and a rectangle

◎ Find the area of the quilt by counting squares

◎ Use proportional reasoning to solve real problems

◎ Use an inch ruler to measure length and width

◎ Find perimeter of quilt

◎ Know a yard is the same as 36 inches

◎ Understand and use fractional words to represent a portion

◎ Use symbols to represent fractions in real situations

◎ Understand concept of half

◎ Skip count by ones, fives, and tens

◎ Make predictions

◎ Use directional words

◎ Represent information collected using tallies

◎ Make a bar graph from information in a chart

◎ Make a Venn diagram

◎ Use bar graph and Venn diagram to answer questions

◎ Add numbers

STUDENT MATERIALS

Per Student:

Quilt Pattern, Legend, and Recording Sheets

Inch ruler

Red, blue, and yellow crayons or markers

TEACHER MATERIALS

Transparencies:
Quilt Pattern, Legend, and Recording Sheets

Venn diagram

Colored dots

PROCEDURE

1. Distribute the Quilt Legend and Pattern to the students and ask them to write their names at the tops of the legend pages. Using the Quilt Legend transparency, guide students on how to respond to statements #1–#6.

2. Have students create their glyphs. Provide assistance, if needed, using the Quilt Pattern transparency.

3. Distribute the Quilt Pattern Recording Sheet and ask students to write their names at the tops of the pages and then complete #1–#9.

4. Discuss #1–#7. For #9, call on several students to share the directions they wrote for the location of an item placed on the quilt. Using the directions, have the class try to identify the item.

5. Post the glyphs.

6. Ask students to compare their predictions given for #7 to the actual responses.

7. Tell students to use the posted glyphs to complete #10.

8. For #11, use the Recording Sheet transparency to guide students on how to make a horizontal bar graph. Go over all the parts of a graph (title, labels on the axes, and the scale). Have students create their graphs and answer #12a–#12d.

9. Post the Venn diagram. When constructing your Venn diagram on a poster, it is recommended that you outline one circle in red and the other circle in blue. Have students do the same on their recording sheets. For example, if the circle labeled "Favorite Holiday: Halloween" is outlined in red, this will help students to understand that anything inside the red circle means that the student's favorite holiday is Halloween.

10. Use information from the glyphs to display each student's response on the Venn. Every student will be represented by a colored dot. If a student selected Valentine's Day as her favorite holiday and dog as her favorite kind of pet, then she will place her dot somewhere on the outside of the two overlapping circles. Tell students to transfer this information onto their recording sheets by placing an "X" to represent the colored dot.

11. Now have students complete #13a–#13e.

EXTENSION

Cut out the individual quilt patterns and tape them together to make one large quilt. Have students find the area of the large quilt. Knowing the length and width of one quilt pattern, students determine the length and width of the large quilt and how many yards of ribbon it would take to go completely around the large quilt.

LITERATURE CONNECTIONS

Sam Johnson and the Blue Ribbon Quilt by Lisa Campbell Ernst

The Quilt Story by Tony Johnston and Tomie dePaola

Where's That Bone? by Lucille Recht Penner, from the Math Matters Series

Quilt Pattern Legend

1. Circle the way you usually get to school.

Bus   **Car**   **Bike**   **Walk**

Beginning at the word "Start" on your Quilt Pattern, do the following:
Move up 2 spaces.
Move right 2 spaces.
Move up 1 space.
Move left 1 space.
Draw the appropriate design in this space.

	Bus	Car	Bike	Walk
Draw this design in the space.	■	●	▲	▬

2. Circle your favorite holiday.

Halloween   **Thanksgiving**   **Valentine's Day**   **Fourth of July**

Beginning at the word "Start," do the following:
Move up 4 spaces.
Move right 3 spaces.
Move up 1 space.
Move left 3 spaces.
Draw the appropriate design in this space.

	Halloween	Thanksgiving	Valentine's Day	Fourth of July
Draw this design in the space.	🎃	🦃	♥	🏴

3. Circle your favorite type of playground equipment.

Swing   **Slide**   **Merry-go-round**   **Monkey bars**

Beginning at the word "Start," do the following:

Move up 2 spaces.

Move right 4 spaces.

Move down 1 space.

Draw the appropriate design in this space.

	Swing	Slide	Merry-go-round	Monkey bars
Draw this design in the space.	⊔	╲	⊕	⊓⊓

4. Circle your favorite kind of pet.

Dog   **Cat**   **Bird**   **Other**

Beginning at the word "Start," do the following:

Move up 1 space.

Move right 3 spaces.

Move up 4 spaces.

Move right 1 space.

Draw the appropriate design in this space.

	Dog	Cat	Bird	Other
Write this letter in the space.	D	C	B	X

5. Beginning at the word "Start," do the following:

Move up 3 spaces.

Move right 2 spaces.

Move up 1 space.

Move left 2 spaces.

Move down 3 spaces.

Write your first name in this space.

6. Color the empty spaces of your quilt using the colors red, blue, and yellow.

Quilt
Pattern

START

NAME: _____

Quilt Pattern
Recording Sheet

1 a. What is the shape of the quilt pattern? _____

   b. How many sides and corners does it have?

   Sides _____   Corners _____

2 a. How is the shape of the spaces inside the quilt like the quilt

   pattern? _____

   _____

   b. How is the shape of the spaces different?

   _____

3. The quilt pattern covers _____ square units. If you connect
   4 quilt patterns together, they would cover a total of _____
   square units.

   Length _____   Width _____

4 a. Using your inch ruler, measure the length and width of the
      quilt pattern.

   b. If you were going to put ribbon completely around your quilt
      pattern, would 1 yard be enough? _____

   c. Explain. _____

   _____

5 a. In your quilt pattern, how many spaces are colored red, blue, or yellow? _____

b. How many spaces are colored red? _____

c. What fraction of the colored spaces is red?

_____   _____
           (words)   (symbol)

d. This fraction is _____ half.
                       (greater than) (less than) (equal to)

e. How do you know? _____

_____

6 a. If a yellow space is worth 1¢, a red space is worth 5¢, and a blue space is worth 10¢, what is the value of your quilt?

_____

b. The value of your quilt is _____ a dollar.
                                   (greater than) (less than) (equal to)

7 a. You had to draw a shape to represent how you usually get to school. Which shape do you think was drawn most? _____

b. What type of transportation does this shape represent?

_____

c. Why do you think that type of transportation was chosen the most?_____

8. Give your teacher the completed quilt pattern.

9. Several items have been placed on this quilt. Write directions from "Start" to the location of one of the items.

_____

_____

_____

_____

Start

I gave directions to the _____.

10. Look at the posted glyphs to fill in the tally chart below.

Favorite Playground Equipment	Tally Marks	Total Votes
Swing		
Slide		
Merry-go-round		
Monkey bars		

11. Use the information in your tally chart to create a bar graph.

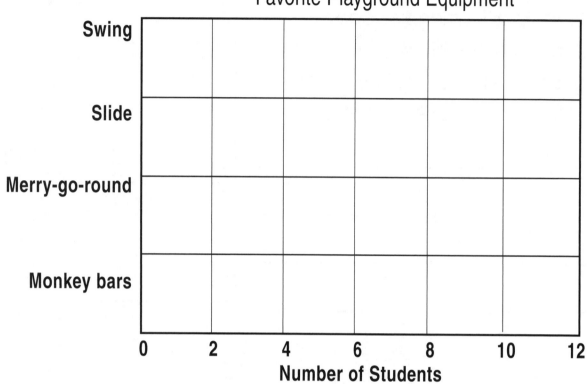

Favorite Playground Equipment

12 a. The number of students who picked monkey bars and swing

is _____ .

b. The number of students who picked slide and merry-go

round is _____ .

c. The number of students who picked slide or swing is_____ .

d. _____ more students picked _____than _____ .

13. Use the class's glyphs to fill in the Venn diagram below.

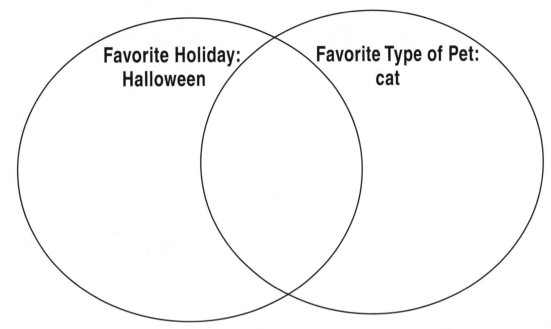

Favorite Holiday: Halloween

Favorite Type of Pet: cat

a. The number of students who chose Halloween as their favorite holiday is _____.

b. The number of students who chose Halloween is

_____ the number of students who

(greater than) (less than) (equal to)

chose another holiday.

c. The number of students who chose a cat as their favorite kind of pet is _____.

d. The number of students who chose cat is _____

(greater than) (less than) (equal to)

the number of students who chose another kind of pet.

e. The number of students who chose Halloween as their favorite holiday and a cat as their favorite kind of pet is _____.

Bare Bear Glyph

OBJECTIVES

- ◎ Create a glyph by answering a survey of questions
- ◎ Collect and interpret data
- ◎ Have an intuitive sense of area; cover surfaces with various objects
- ◎ Use an inch ruler to measure lengths
- ◎ Know that 1 foot =12 inches, 1 yard = 3 feet
- ◎ Use one-to-several correspondence in real situations
- ◎ Collect information and represent it using tally marks
- ◎ Collect information and represent it using a bar graph
- ◎ Be able to separate a set of things into equal groups
- ◎ List possible selections in real situations

STUDENT MATERIALS

Per Student:

Bare Bear Pattern, Legend, Recording Sheets #1 and #2, and Favorite Bear bar graph

Dried beans

Small cups

Inch ruler

Markers or crayons

Scissors

Glue

TEACHER MATERIALS

Transparencies:
Bare Bear Pattern, Legend, and Recording Sheets #1 and #2, and Favorite Bear bar graph

9x12-inch sheet of construction paper

PROCEDURE

1. Distribute the Bare Bear Pattern and Recording Sheet #1 and ask students to write their names at the tops of the sheets. Using your transparency, read aloud and explain #1a–#1d on the recording sheet. Hand out beans and cups to students and ask them to complete #1a–#1d on their recording sheets.

2. Project the pattern transparency and model how to measure the distance across the bear's arms with a ruler. Have students complete #2a on their recording sheets.

3. Hold the sheet of construction paper horizontally and ask students to figure out the number of bears it would take to go across the sheet. Have them complete #2b–#2c on their sheets.

4. Divide students into groups and have them work together solving problems #2d–#2h on their recording sheets. When students have completed this, go over their answers.

5. Distribute the Bare Bear Legend. Have students fill in the blanks, circle the answer to each question, and then create their glyphs.

6. Collect and post their Bear Glyphs.

7. Hand out Recording Sheet #2 and use your transparency for this to guide students on how to make tally marks to record results. Tell students to refer to the posted glyphs to collect information and ask them to fill in #1 on Recording Sheet #2.

8. Hand out the Favorite Bear bar graph sheet and ask students to write their names at the top. Use your transparency of this to guide students in how to make a bar graph. Go over all the parts of a graph (title, labels on each axis, and the scale) and then have the students create their bar graph (#2 on Recording Sheet #2).

9. Ask students to complete #3 on Recording Sheet #2. You may need to hand out beans so that students can decide if they can put the recorded number of votes into two equal groups.

10. Have students complete #4 on Recording Sheet #2.

11. Systematically list all the different uniforms the bear can wear. Try to find a bear glyph of each. Start with the red shirt and list one combination. Then ask if anyone sees a different uniform with the red shirt? Continue until all six uniforms have been found. (You might want to color and cut out all six of the different uniform combinations in case students don't have all of them.)

Red shirt—blue shorts
Red shirt—brown shorts
Blue shirt—blue shorts
Blue shirt—brown shorts
White shirt—blue shorts
White shirt—brown shorts

EXTENSION

Adopt a teddy bear as a class mascot. Use baby doll clothes to dress it. Start off with two shirts and two pairs of shorts. Record each day what the bear is wearing. The next time it is dressed, it must wear something different until all outfits are worn. Then change the clothes choices and repeat the procedure.

LITERATURE CONNECTION

Jesse Bear, What Will You Wear? by Nancy White Carlstrom

NAME: _____

Bare Bear Legend

1. What is your favorite type of bear? _____

	Polar	Grizzly	Black	Panda
Color your bear pattern	**white**	**tan**	**gray**	**black and white**

2. Which of the following is your favorite fairy tale? _____

	Goldilocks and the Three Bears	The Three Little Pigs	Little Red Riding Hood
Color the eyes	**yellow**	**blue**	**green**

3. Have you ever had a teddy bear? _____

	Yes	No
Color the nose	**pink**	**orange**

4. What is your favorite color of uniform shorts? _____

	Blue	Khaki
Color the shorts	**blue**	**brown**

5. What is your favorite color of uniform shirt? _____

	Blue	Red	White
Color the shirt	**blue**	**red**	**white**

6. Cut out your bear pattern and uniform. Glue the uniform on your bear, and write your name on the back.

Bare Bear and Uniform
Pattern

NAME: _____

Bare Bear
Recording Sheet #1

1. a. Estimate the number of beans it would take to cover your bear pattern. My estimate is_____ beans.

   b. Cover your bear pattern with beans. Count the number of beans it took to cover your pattern. The actual number of beans it took to cover the bear pattern was _____.

   c. Explain how you counted the number of beans it took to cover the pattern. _____

   _____

   d. My estimate was _____the actual number of beans.
   (greater than) (less than) (equal to)

2. a. Use a ruler to measure the distance across the bear's arms in inches. The distance across the bear's arms is about _____ inches.

   b. Natalie wants to glue bear patterns along the 12-inch side of a 9x12-inch sheet of construction paper. How many bear patterns will fit across the sheet? _____

   12 inches

   c. Another name for 12 inches is _____

d. The bulletin board is 9 feet long. Natalie wants to put a row of construction paper across the top of the board.
How many sheets of paper will it take to go across the board?

_____ sheets of construction paper

9 feet

e. Natalie puts the construction paper with the bears on the bulletin board. Jacob counted the bear patterns. How many did he count? Jacob counted _____ bear patterns across the bulletin board.

f. There are 3 feet in 1 yard. The bulletin board is 9 feet long. Another way to give the length of the board is to say that it is _____ yards long.

g. How many sheets of construction paper would it take to go across the board below?_____

2 yards

h. How many bear patterns would you need to go across the board?_____

Explain how you got your answer.

_____

_____

NAME: _____

Bare Bear
Recording Sheet #2

1. Fill in the table below looking at the bear glyphs.

Type of Bear	Tally Marks	Total Votes
Polar		
Grizzly		
Black		
Panda		

2. Use the chart above to help you make a bar graph of the students' favorite types of bears.

3. Fill in the chart below.

Name of Fairy Tale	Total Votes	Can I put the number of votes into two equal groups?
Goldilocks and the Three Bears		
Three Little Pigs		
Little Red Riding Hood		

4. There are _____ bears posted.

   a. I see a total of _____noses.

   b. I see a total of _____eyes.

   c. If there were 10 bears posted, I would see _____

   noses and _____eyes.

5. List all the different uniforms the bear could have worn to school.

Shirt Color	Shorts Color	Number of Bears Wearing that Uniform

Favorite Type of Bear
(BAR GRAPH)

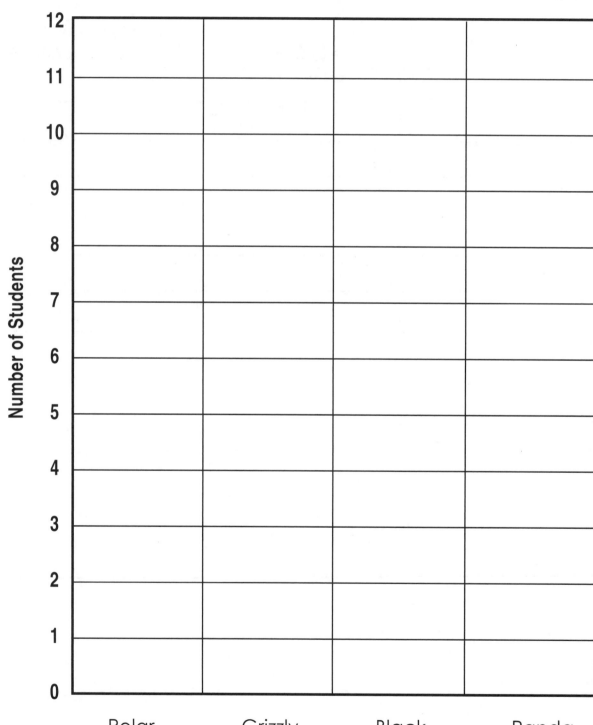

Number of Students

12
11
10
9
8
7
6
5
4
3
2
1
0

Polar   Grizzly   Black   Panda

Types of Bears

Birth Announcement Glyph

OBJECTIVES

- ◎ Create a glyph by answering a survey of questions
- ◎ Collect and represent information using a survey
- ◎ Use inch rulers and tapes to measure length
- ◎ Compare and order numbers
- ◎ Determine if a number is odd or even
- ◎ Find the difference between two numbers
- ◎ Use a scale to measure weight in pounds
- ◎ Know that there are 12 months in a year
- ◎ Know that 1 foot = 12 inches, 1 yard = 36 inches, 1 pound = 16 ounces
- ◎ Read time to 5 minutes
- ◎ Plot birth places on a map of U.S. (and world map if needed)
- ◎ Use proportional reasoning to solve real problems
- ◎ Describe what is more likely, less likely, or equally likely to happen in a real situation
- ◎ Represent information using a line plot

STUDENT MATERIALS

Per Student:

Birth Announcement Pattern, Legend, Recording Sheet, and world map if needed

Markers or crayons

Tape measure

24-inch-long strip of adding machine tape

Scissors

Tape

TEACHER MATERIALS

Transparencies:
Birth Announcement Pattern, Legend, and Recording Sheet

Kitchen scale

Man's large tube sock

10 pounds of rice

Scoop

Funnel

Rubber band

Catch basin

12-month calendar

Map of U.S. (and world map if needed)

Dots or push pins to show locations on the maps

PROCEDURE

1. Distribute the Birth Announcement Pattern. Have students take theirs home and ask their parents or other family member to fill it out.

2. Next day, hand out the Birth Announcement Recording Sheets and have students write their names at the tops of the pages. (If you have students who were born outside the U.S., provide a copy of a world map also.) Divide students into groups of four.

3. Hand out adding machine tape and tape measures. Have each student measure and cut off a strip of paper that represents his length at birth. Then have him record his length and name on the strip. Ask students to compare their birth lengths to 12 inches and 24 inches. Have them complete #1–#2 on their recording sheets.

4. Ask one group to come up and tape their strips on the board from shortest to longest, leaving space between them. Have the next group come up and blend their strips from shortest to longest with those that are posted. Continue until all students have hung their strips. Ask students to complete questions #3a–#3e.

5. Hand out the Birth Announcement Legend, ask students to write their names on it, and then complete their glyphs. Tell students to complete #4 on their recording sheets.

6. Select a student's birth announcement at random and fill a sock with rice to model the child's birth weight. Do this as follows:

   - Put the funnel into the top of the sock.

   - Use the scoop and pour rice into the sock over the catch basin.

   - Weigh it after every couple of scoops to see how close you are to the child's birth weight. Continue until the sock's weight equals the birth weight.

   - Stretch the sock to mimic the length of the child and use a rubber band to close the sock. Example: If the child's length at birth was 19 inches, place the sock on the tape measure and stretch it until it is 19 inches long.

   - Close off the end of the sock with a rubber band and fold back the rest of the sock to represent a cap on the baby.

We did this activity with second grade students and they **loved** it. We made up four birth announcement cards, and they created the baby that represented a particular weight and length. They brought blankets from home, wrapped their babies up, and carried them around all day. They also made rice babies at home. Twenty teachers in our district did this activity, and they were all pleased with how little mess the students made and how much they learned. Students have no idea when you say a baby weighs 8 pounds just how heavy that actually is.

7. Post a 12-month calendar and have students record their birthdays on it. Divide students into groups, assign each group a month, and ask them to plan a class birthday party for that particular month. For each party they will have:

Cupcakes—$2.00

Gallon of punch—$1.00

Cups and ice—$2.00

Party hat for each child who is celebrating his/her birthday—$.50 each

Have students complete #5–#8 on their recording sheets. They must solve the problem of what to do about the students who have birthdays during the summer months.

8. Using the map of the U.S. (and world map if needed), place a dot or push pin in each state or country that represents each student's birth location. Have students complete #9 on their recording sheets.

9. Ask students to complete #10 on their recording sheets to show what time they were born. Have the students arrange themselves in order from midnight until 11:59 P.M. (You might want to use your clothesline for this activity.)

10. Post the glyphs. Have students look at the glyphs and determine all the different information they could collect from them. Ask them to choose a category and make a line plot with the data collected (#11 and #12 on the recording sheet).

11. Using the glyphs, determine if any students were delivered by the same doctor (#13).

12. Have students answer #14 on their recording sheets.

LITERATURE CONNECTIONS

How Big Is a Foot? by Rolf Myller

Weight (Math Counts) by Henry Pluckrose

The 100-Pound Problem by Jennifer Dussling, from the Math Matters Series

Birth Announcement
Legend

1. Are you male or female? _____

	Female	Male
Color the border on your announcement	pink	blue

(Do not color in the circles at the bottom of your announcement!)

2. What was your weight at birth? _____

       Color the number of circles at the bottom of your announcement that is equal to your birth weight rounded to the nearest pound.

3. In which state or country were you born? _____

       Put the first letter of the state or country in which you were born on the front of the block.

4. In which season were you born? _____

	Color of rattle
Fall: Sept., Oct., Nov.	orange
Winter: Dec., Jan., Feb.	blue
Spring: Mar., Apr., May	green
Summer: June, July, Aug.	yellow

Birth Announcement
Pattern

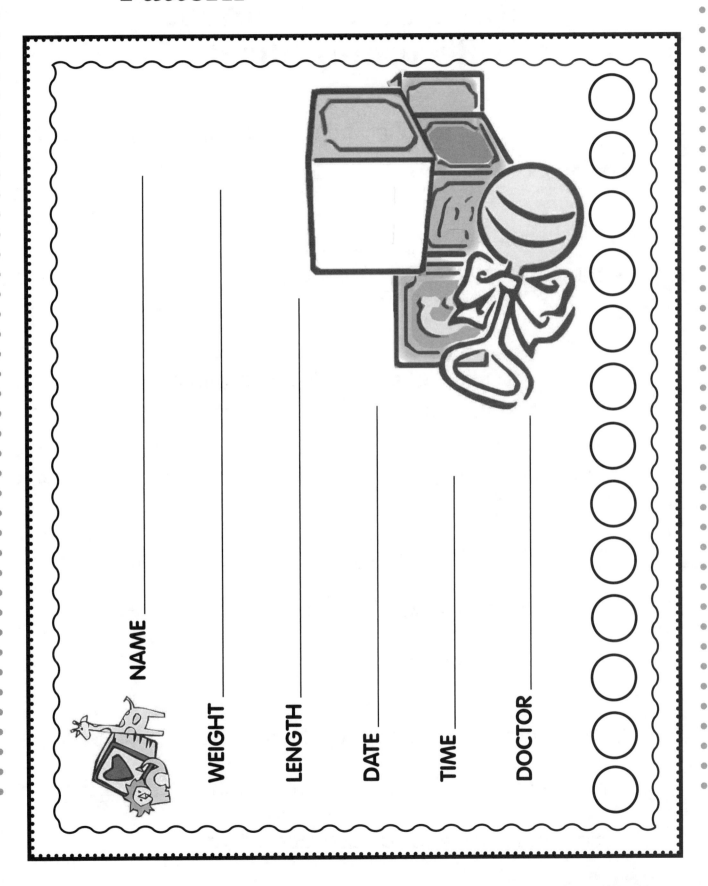

NAME

WEIGHT

LENGTH

DATE

TIME

DOCTOR

NAME: _____

Birth Announcement Recording Sheet

1. I was_____ inches long when I was born. I was _____
(longer) (shorter)
than a foot. I was _____than two feet.
(longer) (shorter)

2. My birth length is an _____number. I know this
(odd) (even)
because I _____ divide_____inches into two equal
(can) (cannot)
groups.

3. Measure and cut a piece of adding machine tape to show your birth length. Write your name on the strip and the length of the strip. As your teacher calls you to the board, place your birth length in the proper place. Strips should be hung from shortest to longest.

   a. The shortest birth length in our class is _____ inches.

   b. The longest birth length in our class is _____ inches.

   c. The difference between the longest and shortest is _____ inches.

   d. The birth length that shows up the most is _____ inches.

   e. If I add up _____'s birth length and _____'s
   (a student's name)   (a student's name)
   birth length, they would equal about 1 yard.

4. Use your legend to color your Birth Announcement Pattern. How much did you weigh at birth?_____ My weight rounded to the nearest pound is_____pounds.

5. Use the calendar below to record each student's birthday during the month your group was assigned.

Sunday	Monday	Tuesday	Wednesday	Thursday	Friday	Saturday

6. You must plan a party to celebrate all the birthdays that take place during that month. The birthday party will have the following:

Cupcakes—$2.00
Gallon of punch—$1.00
Cups and ice—$2.00
Party hat for each child who is celebrating his/her birthday that month—$.50 each

7. Money spent for that month is _____.

8. What should we do for the students who have birthdays during the summer months?

_____

_____

_____

_____

9. Using the United States map below (and a world map if needed,)
   place a dot where each student in your class was born.

10. a. Record your time of birth on both clocks. Were you born in

the morning, afternoon, or evening? _____

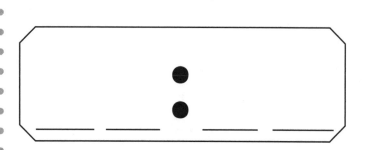

A.M.   P.M

b. Circle A.M. or P.M.

11. Look at the posted glyphs. List different ways we could
    organize the glyphs. Example: male or female

_____

_____

_____

12. Sort the glyphs by a category. Write the characteristics below the line. Place an "X" above each characteristic to represent how many students have that characteristic.

_____

13. Were any students in the class delivered by the same doctor?_____

14. There are _____ boys in our class. There are _____ girls in our class. Pretend we put the glyphs into a bag, and pull out one without looking. We are _____ likely to pull a boy's
(more) (less) (equally)
glyph as a girl's glyph.

Name Tag Glyph

OBJECTIVES

- ◎ Create a glyph by answering a survey of questions
- ◎ Identify a 2-D shape by number of sides and corners
- ◎ Compare and contrast the attributes of quadrilaterals
- ◎ Use an inch ruler to measure length and width
- ◎ Find the perimeter of a figure
- ◎ Know a yard is the same as 36 inches
- ◎ Understand and use fractional words to represent a portion
- ◎ Use symbols to represent fractions in situations
- ◎ Understand the concept of half
- ◎ Understand the inverse relationship of addition and subtraction
- ◎ Recognize figures that are exactly alike
- ◎ Understand concept of symmetry and apply it to a given shape
- ◎ Use information given to make predictions
- ◎ Add with or without regrouping
- ◎ Write money using "$" and "." as well as "¢"
- ◎ Recognize, count, and determine change using pennies, nickels, dimes, and quarters
- ◎ Represent a value using different combinations of coins
- ◎ Compare and order values
- ◎ Round values to the nearest 10¢
- ◎ Represent information using a circle graph
- ◎ Describe what is more likely, less likely, or certain to happen

STUDENT MATERIALS

Per Student:

Name Tag Pattern, Legend, and Recording Sheets #1, #2, and #3

Markers or crayons

Inch ruler

Scissors

TEACHER MATERIALS:

Transparencies: Name Tag Pattern, Legend, and Recording Sheets #1, #2, and #3

Yardstick

Bag for the tiles

Five signs on cardstock: "1 or 2," "3 or 4," "5 or 6," "7 or 8," "9 or more"

Clothesline and clothespins

4x6-inch index cards for number line: $.00 $.10 $.20 $.30 $.40 $.50 $.60 $.70 $.80 $.90 $1.00

Store with items priced from $.03 to $1.50

Play coins

Two different colors of tiles

Adding machine tape

PROCEDURE

1. Distribute the Name Tag Pattern, Recording Sheet #1, and inch ruler to each student.

2. Have students write their names on the recording sheet and complete #1–#5.

3. Project your transparency of this sheet and discuss the answers to #1–#5.

4. Distribute the Name Tag Legend. Ask students to create their glyphs, and complete #6–#8 on Recording Sheet #1. (Explain to students that when figures are the same shape and size, they are said to be congruent. Also, review symmetry.)

5. Place the five signs in different areas of the classroom.

   a. Ask students to predict the smallest number of letters used to represent the first name of a student(s) in the class.

   b. Ask students to predict the largest number of letters used to represent the name of a student(s) in the class.

   c. Ask students to predict which number of letters will occur most often.

   d. Have students move to the area designated for the number of letters in their first name, then direct each group to subdivide into a single-number group. (For example, "5 or 6" subdivides into "5" and "6.") Tell students they can now check their predictions.

6. Distribute Name Tag Recording Sheet #2 and have students write their names on the pages, and then complete it using their glyphs. (You might want to work out a complete chart of corresponding letters and monetary values ahead of time.)

7. Call on two students. Ask them to use their glyphs to compare the value of their names and to line up in order. Instruct them to use the words "less than," "greater than," or "equal to" when comparing their values. Repeat the procedure four more times with two different students.

8. Call on three students. Have them compare their values and line up in order. Tell students to use the words "less than," "greater than," or "equal to" when comparing their values. Repeat the procedure four more times with three different students.

9. Have these last three students remain in the front of the room, and call on another student. Tell her to compare her first name's value to that of the three students and decide where to line up. Instruct her to use the words "less than," "greater than," or "equal to" when comparing her value to the other values. (You may want to use a clothesline to place values.) Continue the procedure until the entire class has lined up in order according to the value of their first names, or until all the values have been placed in order on the clothesline.

10. Pose these questions to the students:

    - Which name has the least value?
    - Which name has the greatest value?
    - Are there any names with the same value? Do the names consist of the same number of letters?
    - Can we say that longer names have greater values?
    - What can you tell me about a name that is worth a lot?

11. Ask students now to round the values of their first names, and then pose these questions:

    - I have one coin in my pocket, and it is worth 10¢. What coin is in my pocket?
    - If I had two dimes, what would the value be? Six dimes?
    - How many dimes are needed to equal a dollar? Have students count by tens to prove that it takes 10 dimes to equal a dollar.

12. Set up a number line using the index cards, clothesline, and clothespins. Call one student up at a time. Have the student say which two dime values his name value is between and which dime value his name is closer to. (For example: Larry has a value of $.84. The student should say that $.84 is between $.80 and $.90. It is 4¢ away from 80 and 6¢ away from 90 so it is closer to $.80.). Have him use clothespins or tape to attach his name tag to the closer tenth. Continue until all students have rounded the values of their first names. (If a student's first name is greater than $1.00, then you will have to include a card for $1.10, $1.20, etc.)

Note: Do not teach students to round down when a number ends in a 0–4 and to round up when a number ends in a 5–9. Instead, the only rule they need to know is this: when a number ends in a 5, it is an equal distance from both multiples of 10, so round <u>up</u> to the nearest multiple of 10.

13. Pose this question: What are all the values that would round to $.60?

14. Distribute Recording Sheet #3 to the students and have them write their names at the top. Use the scenario that the students are buying something from the classroom store that is equal to or less than the value of their first names. Use the value of your first name to instruct students on how to complete their recording sheets.

15. Call one student up at a time. Ask her to select an item she wants to purchase and to figure out what coins will be used to pay for that item. Then have her figure out the change she should receive and complete the number sentences. Next, have her complete Recording Sheet #3.

16. With the name tags posted, ask the following questions:

    - How many students have a name that begins with a vowel?
    - How many students have a name that begins with a consonant?

17. Place tiles of one color in a bag to equal the number of names that begin with a vowel; place tiles of another color to equal the number of names that begin with a consonant.

18. Pose these questions:

- Which color tile am I <u>least likely</u> to pull out of the bag?
- Which color tile am I <u>more likely</u> to pull out of the bag?
- Which color tile am I <u>certain</u> to pull out of the bag?

19. Ask students to form a Human Circle Graph. Have those who have more vowels than consonants in their first name hold hands. Then have those who have more consonants than vowels in their first name hold hands. Finally, have students who have an equal number of vowels and consonants hold hands.

20. Before you ask the groups to form a large circle, pose the following questions:

- Which section of the circle will be the largest and why?
- Which section will be the smallest and why?
- Will there be equal sections? How do you know?

21. Ask the groups (still holding hands) to form a large circle. Stand in the center, and using adding machine tape, subdivide the circle into three sections.

Pose these questions:

- Which section is the largest?
- Which section is the smallest?

EXTENSIONS

a. Have students estimate the sums and differences of two students' first names.
b. Have students determine the values of their last names and then complete procedure steps #5–#11 again.
c. Have students find a word that has a value of $1.00.

LITERATURE CONNECTIONS

Where the Sidewalk Ends, "Smart," by Shel Silverstein

Probably Pistachio by Stuart J. Murphy

Let's Fly a Kite by Stuart J. Murphy

Name Tag Legend

1. Does your first name begin with a vowel or a consonant?

   _____

	Vowel	Consonant
Write your name on the top dotted line.	**red**	**green**

2. How many letters are in your first name? _____

	1 or 2	3 or 4	5 or 6	7 or 8	9 or more
Color the border	**green**	**orange**	**red**	**yellow**	**blue**

3. a. How many vowels are in your first name? _____

   b. How many consonants are in your first name? _____

	More Vowels	More Consonants	Equal
Draw a shape around your name.	**oval**	**rectangle**	**no shape**

Name Tag Pattern

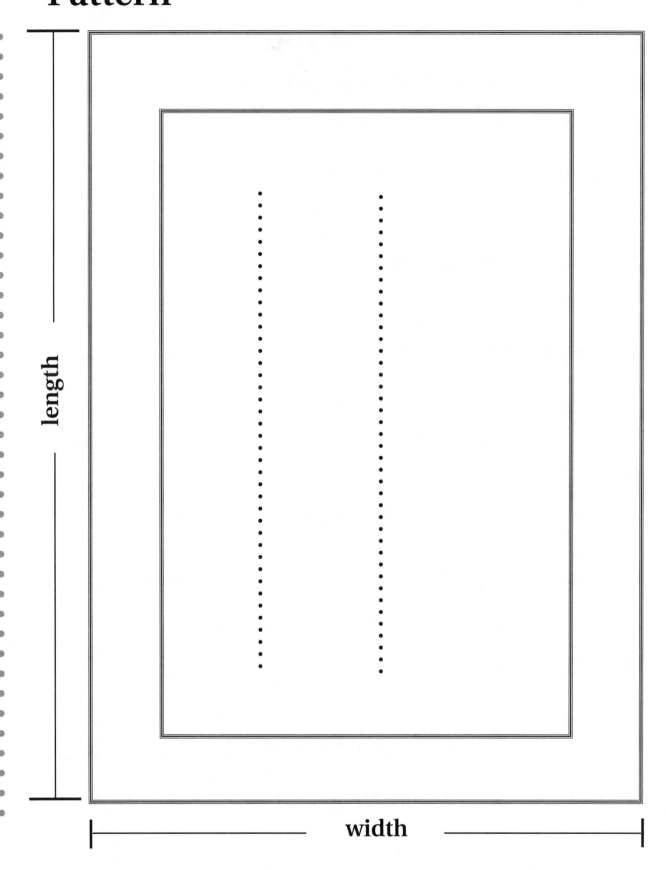

length

width

NAME: _____

Name Tag
Recording Sheet #1

1. What is the shape of the Name Tag Pattern? _____

   a. How many sides does the shape have? _____

   b. How many corners does the shape have? _____

   c. Name a shape that has the same number of sides and corners

     as this pattern. _____

   d. How are the two shapes different? _____

   _____

2. Using a ruler, measure the length and width of the pattern in inches.

   Length _____ Width _____

3. If you were going to trim the Name Tag Pattern with gold ribbon,

   would a yard of ribbon be enough? _____

   Why or why not? _____

4. How many letters are in your first name? _____

   a. What <u>fraction</u> of your first name is made up of vowels?

   _____   _____
       (words)   (symbol)

b. What <u>fraction</u> of your first name is made up of consonants?

_____   _____
(words)   (symbol)

c. The fraction that represents the number of consonants in

your name is _____½.
(less than) (greater than) (equal to)

d. How do you know? _____

5. Complete the number sentences.

_____ **+** _____ **=** _____
(number of   (number of   (number of letters
vowels)   consonants)   in first name)

_____ **-** _____ **=** _____
(number of letters   (number of   (number of vowels)
in first name)   consonants)

6. Using your Name Tag Legend, create your glyph and cut it out.

7. a. Is your Name Tag Glyph the same shape and size as your

neighbor's?_____

b. Are the Name Tag Glyphs congruent? _____

8. Does the Name Tag Glyph have a line of symmetry? _____
If it does, draw the line of symmetry on the back of the glyph.

Name Tag
Recording Sheet #2

1. Imagine that letter "A" has a value of 1¢, "B" has a value of 2¢, "C" has a value of 3¢, "D" has a value of 4¢, and so on.

   a. Predict which classmate's first name will have the greatest value. _____

   b. Predict which classmate's first name will have the least value.

   _____

   c. On the back of your Name Tag Pattern, determine the value of your first name.

   d. On the front of the pattern and on the <u>bottom</u> dotted line, write the value of your first name two ways.
   (Example: 54¢ and $.54)

2. The value of my first name is _____.

   a. Complete the table to show different ways you could represent the value of your first name.

Quarters	Dimes	Nickels	Pennies

   b. Which combination uses the fewest coins?

3. At the bottom of your name tag and using the fewest coins possible, draw the combination that represents the value of your first name.

Name Tag
Recording Sheet #3

1. My first name is _____.

2. The value of my name is _____ or _____.

3. I bought _____ for _____.

4. Draw the coins you gave your partner to pay for the item.

5. Did you get back any change? _____

   If you did, draw your change using the fewest coins possible.

6. Fill in these number sentences.

$$\underset{\text{(cost of item)}}{\rule{2cm}{0.4pt}} + \underset{\text{(change)}}{\rule{2cm}{0.4pt}} = \underset{\text{(amount paid)}}{\rule{2cm}{0.4pt}}$$

$$\underset{\text{(amount paid)}}{\rule{2cm}{0.4pt}} - \underset{\text{(cost of item)}}{\rule{2cm}{0.4pt}} = \underset{\text{(change)}}{\rule{2cm}{0.4pt}}$$

$$\underset{\text{(amount paid)}}{\rule{2cm}{0.4pt}} - \underset{\text{(change)}}{\rule{2cm}{0.4pt}} = \underset{\text{(cost of item)}}{\rule{2cm}{0.4pt}}$$

Pour Me Some More Glyph

OBJECTIVES

- ◎ Create a glyph by answering a survey of questions
- ◎ Collect and represent information from surveys
- ◎ Identify how many fourths have been shaded in a picture
- ◎ Write fraction words
- ◎ Compare fractions to one-half
- ◎ Learn numerical comparisons between cups, pints, and quarts
- ◎ Make a diagram
- ◎ Distinguish between odd and even numbers
- ◎ Make a bar graph from information in a chart
- ◎ Use a bar graph to answer questions
- ◎ Compare and order numbers
- ◎ Add numbers

STUDENT MATERIALS

Per Student:

Pour Me Some More Pattern, Legend, and Recording Sheets

Markers or crayons

Scissors

Tape

TEACHER MATERIALS

Transparencies:
Pour Me Some More Pattern, Legend, and Recording Sheets

Rice, dried beans, or packing peanuts (optional)

1-cup, 1-pint, 1-quart, and 1-liter containers (optional)

PROCEDURE

1. Distribute the Pour Me Some More Legend and Pattern and ask students to write their names on the legend pages. Using your transparencies, model what to do.

2. Have students fill in the blanks and circle their answers to the questions on the legend and use this information to create their glyphs.

3. Hand out the recording sheets. Have students write their names on the pages and ask them to complete questions #1–#2. Use your recording sheet transparency to discuss their answers.

4. Collect and post the glyphs. Talk about #1 on their recording sheets. Remind students that in order for them to write a fraction, something has to be divided into equal parts or it must be a part of a set. Go over all the different fractions students could have written from one-fourth to four-fourths. A student might also see the connection that two-fourths is the same as one-half.

5. Ask the students to use the posted glyphs to complete #3–#7 on their recording sheets. Using your recording sheet transparency, discuss their answers.

6. Have students complete #8–#10 on their recording sheets. This could be assigned for homework after students have filled in the chart (#8).

EXTENSIONS

a. Set aside some time to let students experiment with filling empty containers with rice, beans, or packing peanuts and counting the cups, pints, or quarts it takes to fill them. After doing this hands-on activity, use the glyph to reinforce the idea that 1 pint = 2 cups and 1 quart = 4 cups. There is nothing more valuable than having the students work with the materials so they can learn to estimate about how much a container will hold.

b. Obtain two 1-liter water bottles and a 1-quart bottle of Gatorade. Empty one water bottle and then add food coloring to the water in the other 1-liter bottle, which makes it easier to see the water level. Ask students, "Which do you think holds more, a quart or a liter container?" Most of them will vote for the quart because they note that it is shorter and much "fatter" than the liter bottle. Then ask them, "Why is it hard to compare the two?" (The containers have different shapes.) Next, pour the Gatorade into the empty water bottle, using a funnel. Students are then able to compare the liquids in the same type containers and see that a liter bottle holds just a little more than a quart.

LITERATURE CONNECTIONS

Capacity (Math Counts) by Henry Pluckrose

Room for Ripley by Stuart J. Murphy

Pour Me Some More
Legend

1. What is your favorite type of drink? _____

Favorite Type of Drink	Color of Liquid in Pitcher
Sprite or 7-Up	green
Kool-Aid	red
Coke, Pepsi, Dr. Pepper, or Mr. Pibb	brown
Other	blue

2. What is your favorite fast food? _____

Favorite Fast Food	Number of Cups to Color
Taco	1 cup
Hamburger	2 cups
Pizza	3 cups
Other	4 cups

3. What is your favorite dessert? _____

Favorite Dessert	Color of Handle
Pie	orange
Cookies	blue
Cake	yellow

Pour Me Some More
Pattern

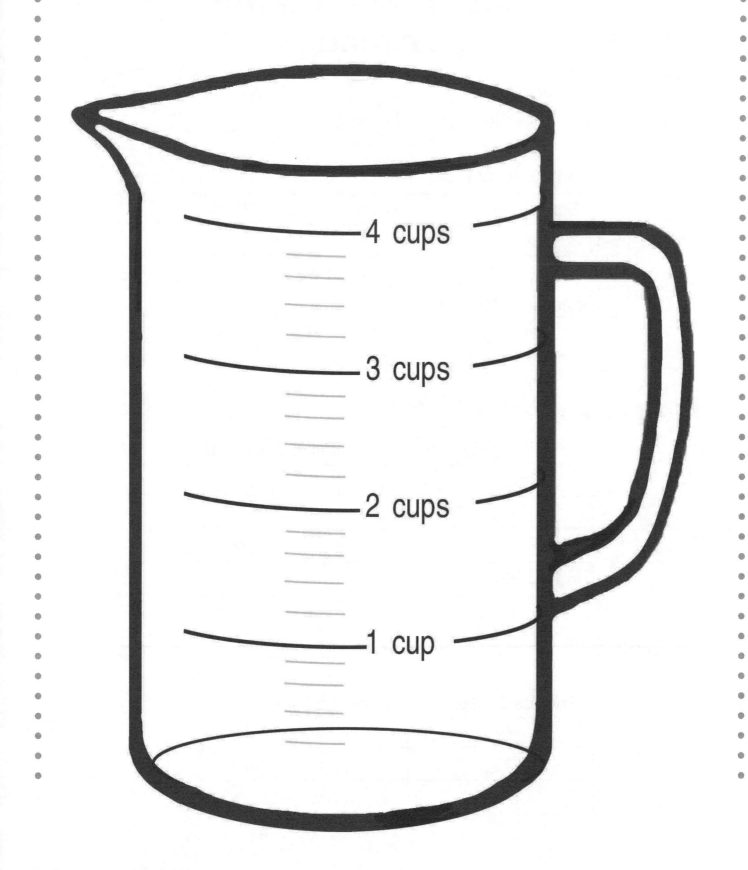

4 cups

3 cups

2 cups

1 cup

NAME: _____

Pour Me Some More
Recording Sheet

1. Look at your glyph to complete the sentences below.

    a. My pitcher will hold _____cups.

    b. I colored _____out of four equal parts.

    c. My pitcher is _____full.
                             (fraction word)

    d. My pitcher is _____full.
                    (less than half) (half) (more than half) (completely)

    e. One pint is the same as _____cups.

    f. One quart is the same as _____cups.

    g. The liquid in my pitcher is _____ a pint.
                         (more than) (less than) (equal to)

    h. The liquid in my pitcher is _____ a quart.
                         (more than) (less than) (equal to)

2. Cut out your glyph, write your name on the back, and give it to your teacher.

3. How many students like the following as their favorite drink?

a. Sprite or 7-Up_____   b. Kool-Aid _____

c. Coke, Pepsi, Dr. Pepper,   d. Other _____
   or Mr. Pibb _____

4. Using the information in #3, write the name of the drink (or drinks) in the correct place on the diagram below.

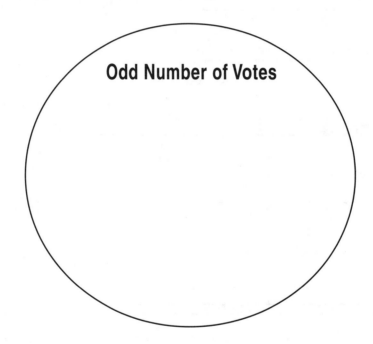

Odd Number of Votes

5. Fill in the tally chart below.

Favorite Fast Food	Tally Marks	Total Votes
Taco		
Hamburger		
Pizza		
Other		

6. Use the information in your chart to create a bar graph.

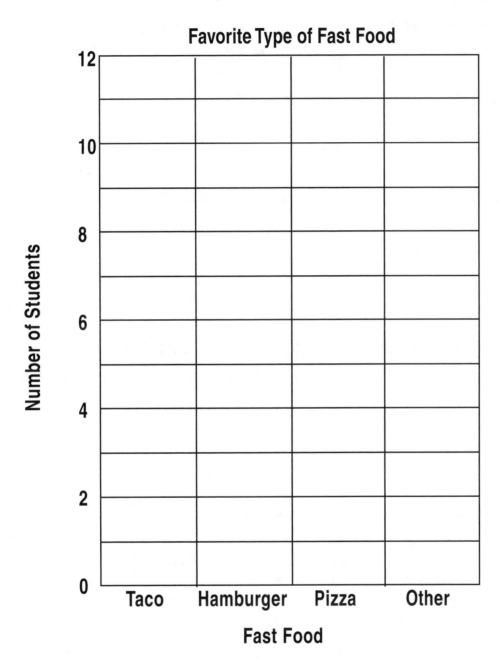

7. Use your bar graph to answer the questions below.

   a. What fast food received the most votes?_____

   b. How many people voted for taco and hamburger? _____

c. How many people voted for pizza? _____

Pizza received an _____ number of votes.
(odd)   (even)

d. How many more people voted for hamburger than other? _____

e. How many people voted? _____

f. Why would we want to know this information?

_____

_____

g. Do you think that the students in the class next door would
have the same results if they made a bar graph of their
favorite fast foods? Explain your answer.

_____

_____

_____

8. Fill in the table below.

Type of Dessert	Number of Votes
Pie	
Cookies	
Cake	

9 a. Put the number of votes for favorite dessert in order below
       from least to greatest.

       _____

       _____

   b. Explain how you put your numbers in order.

       _____

       _____

10 a. The number of people who voted for pie or cake is

       _____.

   b. The number of people who voted for cake or cookies is

       _____.

   c. The number of people who voted for cookies or pie is

       _____.

   d. _____more people voted for _____

       than for _____.